Edition Schott

Carl Czerny

1791 – 1857

Schule der Geläufigkeit

School of Velocity · Ecole de la Vélocité

für Piano
for Piano

opus 299

Herausgegeben von / Edited by / Edité par
Wilhelm Ohmen

ED 9823
ISMN 979-0-001-13815-4

www.schott-music.com

Mainz · London · Berlin · Madrid · New York · Paris · Prague · Tokyo · Toronto
© 2006 SCHOTT MUSIC GmbH & Co. KG, Mainz · Printed in Germany

Inhalt / Contents / Contenu

Heft 3 / Book 3 / Cahier 3

Molto allegro ♩ = 80   56

21

Molto allegro ♩ = 132   58

22

Molto allegro ♩. = 88   60

23

Molto allegro ♩ = 80   63

24

Molto allegro ♩ = 144   66

25

Allegro ♩. = 69   68

26

Allegro ♩. = 69   71

26a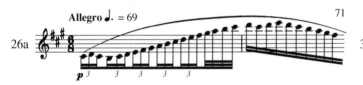

Presto ♩ = 152   74

27

Presto ♩ = 104-112   76

28

Molto allegro ♩ = 144   78

29

Presto volante ♩. = 58   80

30

Heft 4 / Book 4 / Cahier 4

Molto allegro ♩. = 56   82

31

Presto volante ♩ = 88   86

32

Molto allegro e veloce ♩ = 108   88

33

Allegro molto vivo ed energico ♩ = 80   90

34

Allegro vivacissimo ♩. = **92**   93

35

Presto ♩ = 80   94

36

Molto allegro e giocoso ♪ = 138   98

37

Molto allegro, quasi presto ♩ = 144   101

38

Presto (à la Galopade) ♩ = 80   104

39

Allegrissimo, quasi presto ♩ = 96   107

40

Vorwort

Carl Czerny wurde am 20. Februar 1791 in Wien als Sohn des geschätzten Klavierlehrers Wenzel Czerny geboren. Seine Heimatstadt verließ er nur selten und starb dort am 15. Juli 1857. Unterrichtet und geprägt von seinem Vater begann er schon im Alter von drei Jahren Klavier zu spielen und wurde, dank seiner hohen Begabung, aber auch seines großen Fleißes wegen, als Neunjähriger Schüler Ludwig van Beethovens. Dessen Werke spielte er öffentlich und gab sie später heraus. Für Generationen von Pianisten geben diese Ausgaben, seine überlieferten Erläuterungen, vor allem auch seine Schrift *Über den richtigen Vortrag der sämtlichen Beethoven'schen Klavierwerke* (Universal Edition Wien, UE 13340) wichtige Hinweise und Anregungen für deren Interpretation.

Czerny war ein leidenschaftlicher Komponist. Er hinterlies mehr als eintausend Werke. Neben seinen Etüden-sammlungen, bei denen eine Opuszahl oft aus fünfzig oder mehr Stücken besteht, komponierte er Messen, Opern, Orchester-, Klavier- und kammermusikalische Werke in sensiblem frühromantischen Stil. Igor Strawinsky spricht vom *blutvollen Musiker Czerny*, den er noch *höher schätze als den bedeutenden Pädagogen*. Czerny war schon in jungen Jahren ein anerkannter und sehr gefragter Klavierpädagoge. Zahlreiche Klavierschüler und Pianisten bildete er aus, darunter auch Franz Liszt.

Bedeutend und unübersehbar aber sind sein Etüdenwerk und seine klaviermethodischen Schriften. Sein Ziel war es, alle möglichen, damals bekannten spieltechnischen Figuren und Bewegungsabläufe grundlegend darzustellen und für den Unterricht einzurichten. Seine Sammlungen reichen von den ersten Fingerübungen und Studien für den Anfänger bis hin zu ausgedehnten Etüden höchsten Schwierigkeitsgrades. *Fleiß und Übung sind die einzigen Garanten zum Erfolg* – so Czerny. Er fordert aber auch die sensible, einfühlsame musikalische Interpretation, die *Schönheit des Vortrags und Gefühls, welche dem einfachen Gesange zukommen.*

Die vorliegende Ausgabe der „Schule der Geläufigkeit" ist als Fortsetzung der „Vorschule der Geläufigkeit" (Schott ED 9823) für den fortgeschrittenen, technisch versierten Klavierspieler gedacht. Die Stücke sind etwa in aufsteigender Schwierigkeit angeordnet.

Heft 1 besteht hauptsächlich aus Übungen für Tonleitern, gebrochene Akkorde und Arpeggien. Stück Nr. 10 bietet Phrasierung einer Melodie mit schnellen Albertischen Bässen (Begleitfiguren). In den Heften 2 – 4 werden anspruchs-vollere Spielfiguren und Techniken - oft für beide Hände gleichzeitig oder abwechselnd – behandelt:
Gebrochene Terzsequenzen (Nr. 11), Unisono-Arpeggien (Nr. 12), schnelle gebrochene Intervalle (Nr. 13, 20), Chromatik (Nr. 15, 31), Triolen (Nr. 16, 18), gehaltene Melodietöne (Nr. 17, 27), gebrochene Akkorde (Nr. 19), Repetitionen (Nr. 20), Leggiero (Nr. 23), schnelle Sequenzen im Dreitonraum (Nr. 24), Unisono-Tonleitern (Nr. 25), schnelle gebrochene Oktaven (Nr. 28, 35), weite Arpeggien (Nr. 30), Arpeggien im überschlagenden Wechsel der Hände (Nr. 31), gespiegelte Skalen und Sequenzen (Nr. 36), weite Griffe (Nr. 37), Terzen und Doppelgriffe (Nr. 38), Charakteretüde in Des-Dur (Nr. 39).

Die Etüde Nr. 26 ist in zwei Fassungen gedruckt. Um eine leichtere Synchronisierung beider Hände zu ermöglichen, können die Skalen der rechten Hand rhythmisch eingeteilt werden, wie in Nr. 26a vom Herausgeber vorgeschlagen.

Nr. 34 ist eine Etüde vorwiegend für die linke Hand. Sie weist in ihrer kraftvollen Harmonik und bravourösen Aussage schon auf die kunstvollen Konzertetüden der Romantik hin und würde ihre Wirkung im Konzertsaal nicht verfehlen.

Die Metronomzahlen und Fingersätze stammen vom Herausgeber. Sie sind der Spielart auf heutigen Klavieren mit moderner Mechanik angepasst, denn die Instrumente der damaligen Zeit mit Wiener Mechanik hatten einen leichteren Anschlag, eine engere Oktavspanne und kürzere Vordertasten. Fingersätze in Klammern können alternativ angewen-det werden; sie ermöglichen teilweise eine bequemere Ausführung. Alle Übungen sollen langsam einstudiert und im Tempo gesteigert werden. Auch bei Nichterreichen des vorgeschlagenen Zeitmaßes werden sie von Nutzen sein. Diese Stücke sind als begleitende Übungen zur Bewältigung der anspruchsvollen virtuosen Klavierliteratur aller Epochen sehr hilfreich.

Wilhelm Ohmen

Preface

Carl Czerny was born in Vienna on 20 February 1791 and lived there until his death on 15 July 1857, rarely leaving the city of his birth. His father was the respected piano teacher Wenzel Czerny, under whose instruction and influence Carl started playing the piano at the age of three; thanks to the boy's remarkable gifts and hard work, Ludwig van Beethoven took him on as a pupil when he was only nine. Carl Czerny performed Beethoven's works in public and later published them: these editions with their accompanying explanations, and in particular Czerny's writings *On the correct way to perform all Beethoven's piano works* (Universal Edition Vienna, UE 13340) have been a source of essential advice and inspiration for generations of pianists.

Czerny was a prolific composer who left behind him more than a thousand works. Besides his collections of studies, where a single opus number often represents fifty or more pieces, he composed masses, operas, orchestral, piano and chamber music works in the early Romantic style. Igor Stravinsky speaks of *Czerny the red-blooded musician,* whom he rated even *higher than as an influential teacher*. Even as a young man, Czerny was recognised and much in demand as a piano teacher. He taught many pupils and trained a number of pianists, including Franz Liszt.

His major legacy, however, is the studies and tutorial works he wrote for the piano. It was Czerny's aim to give an outline presentation of all the figures and patterns of notes that pianists in his day were likely to encounter and to arrange them for tuition purposes. His collections of studies range from initial finger exercises for beginners to extensive and extremely difficult studies. *Hard work and plenty of practice are the only reliable paths to success,* according to Czerny. He also called for sensitive musical interpretation, though: the *beauty of playing and the sensitivity that approaches the simplicity of song.*

This edition of "Exercises in articulation" is intended as a continuation of "Preliminary exercises in articulation" (Schott ED 9823) for the advanced, technically accomplished pianist. The pieces are presented in approximate order of increasing difficulty.

Volume 1 consists chiefly of exercises based on scales, broken chords and arpeggios. Piece No. 10 involves phrasing a melody with rapid *Alberti* bass accompaniment. In volumes 2 – 4 more demanding figures and techniques are introduced, often for both hands at the same time or in alternation:
sequences of broken thirds (No. 11), unison arpeggios (No. 12), rapid broken intervals (Nos. 13 & 20), chromatic progressions (Nos. 15 & 31), triplets (Nos. 16 & 18), legato melodies (Nos. 17 &27), broken chords (No. 19), repeated notes (No. 20), playing *leggiero* (No. 23), rapid sequences in thirds (No. 24), unison scales (No. 25), rapid octave leaps (Nos. 28 & 35), extensive arpeggios (No. 30), arpeggios with the hands crossing over (No. 31), scales and sequences in contrary motion (No. 36), reaching across large intervals (No. 37), thirds and parallel intervals (No. 38) and a character study in Db major (No. 39). Study No. 26 is printed in two versions. To make it easier to synchronise both hands, the scales in the right hand may be divided up rhythmically as suggested by the editor in No. 26a. No. 34 is a study primarily for the left hand. Its powerful harmonies and bravura style already hint at the sophisticated concert studies of the Romantic era and would not be out of place in the concert hall.

Metronome figures and fingerings are by the editor. These are designed to suit playing on modern pianos and their mechanism – the Viennese instruments of Czerny's day had a lighter touch, a narrower octave span and shorter white keys. Fingerings in brackets may be used as alternatives; some of them may be found more comfortable. All the exercises should be played slowly at first, then at gradually increased speed. Even if the suggested tempo is never achieved, they will still be useful. These pieces will be very helpful as auxiliary exercises in meeting the demands of the virtuoso piano repertoire of any era.

Wilhelm Ohmen
English translation Julia Rushworth

Die Schule der Geläufigkeit

Op. 299

Heft 1 / Book 1 / Cahier 1

Carl Czerny
1791–1857

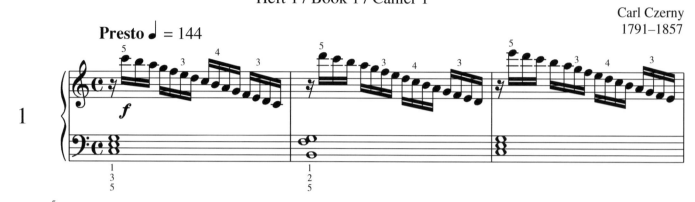

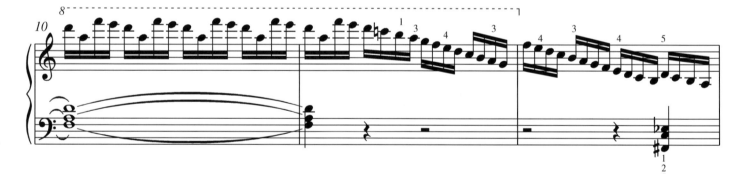

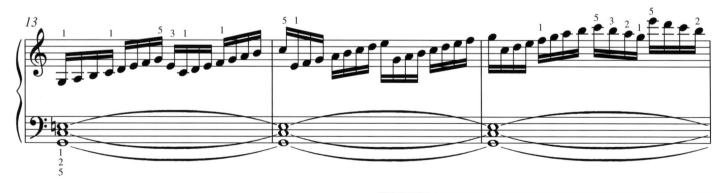

© 2006 Schott Music GmbH & Co. KG, Mainz

51 676

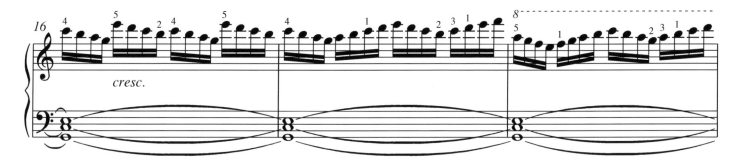

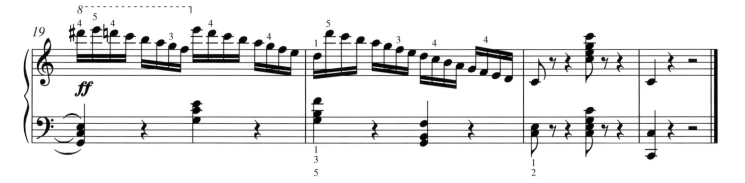

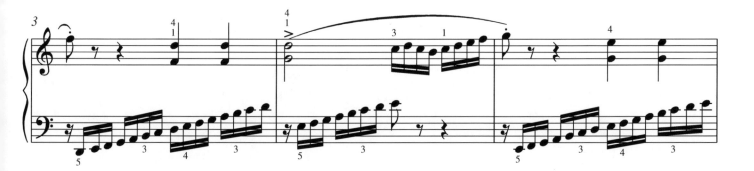

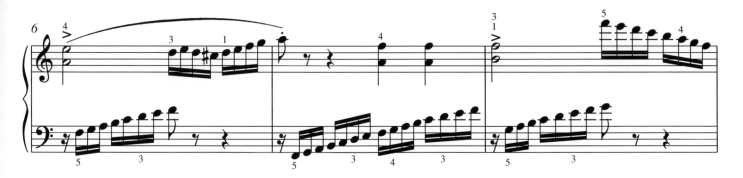

10

Presto ♩ = 160

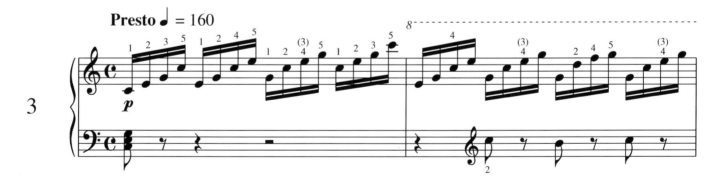

3

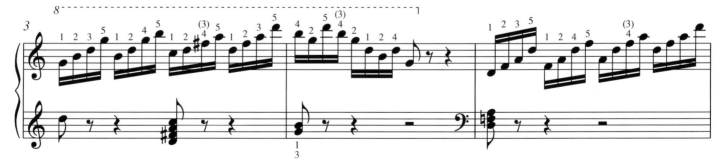

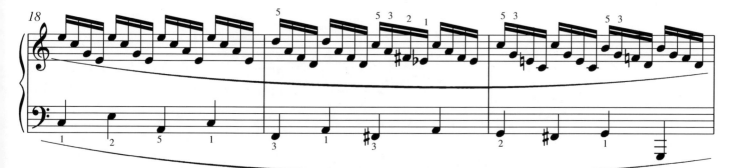

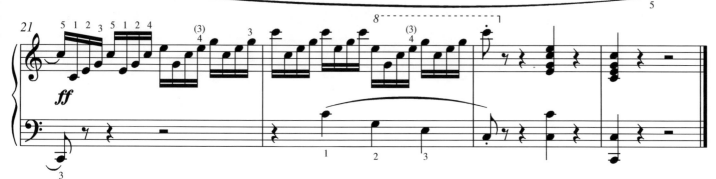

12

Presto ♩. = 108

4

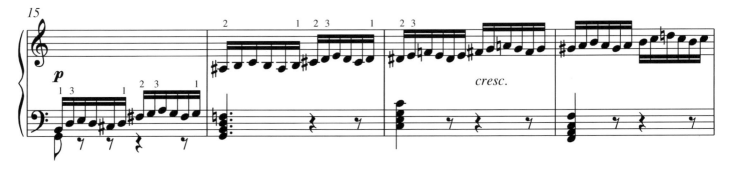

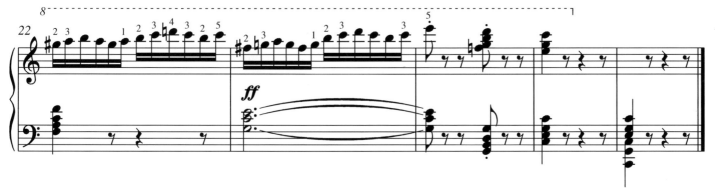

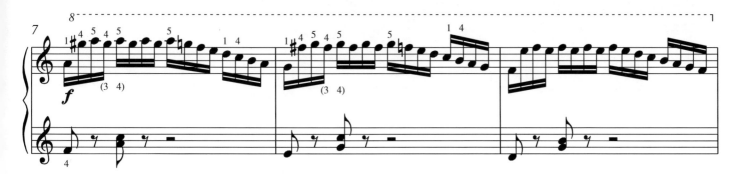

Molto allegro ♩ = 160

6

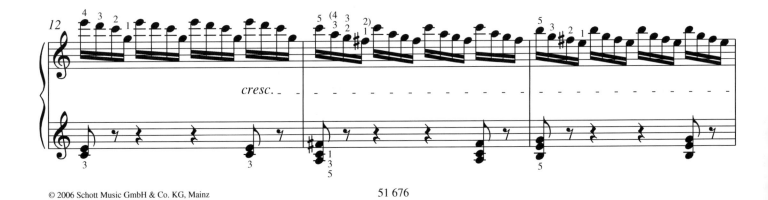

51 676

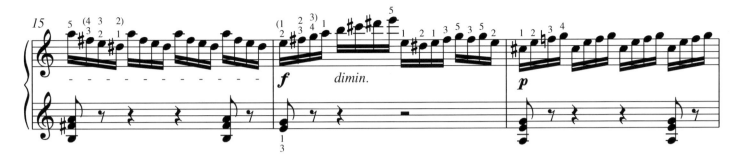

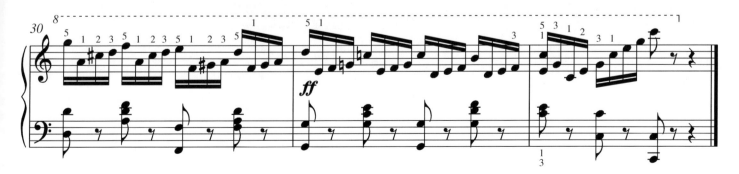

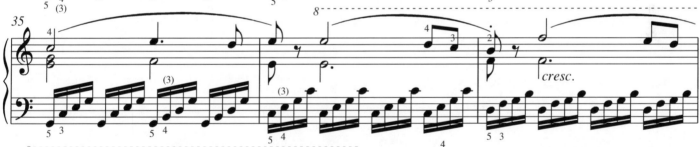

Molto allegro ♩ = 144

8

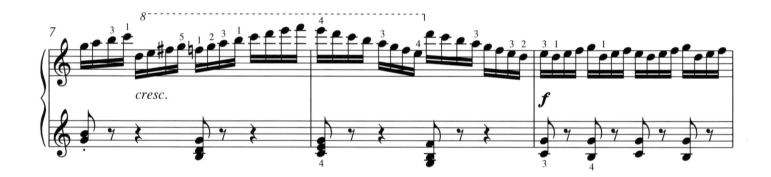

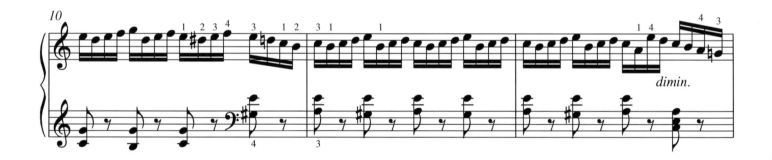

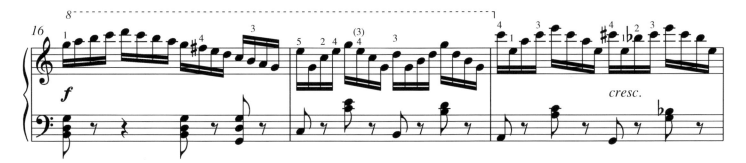

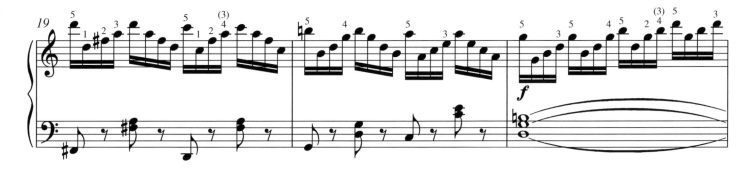

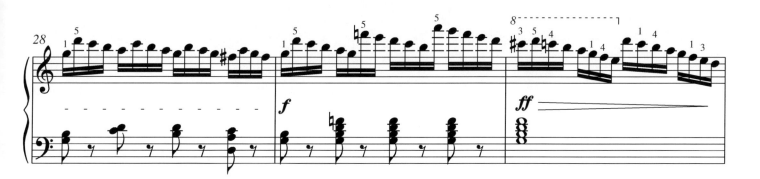

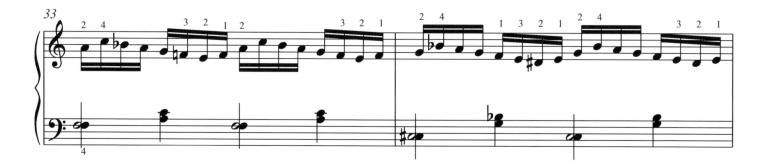

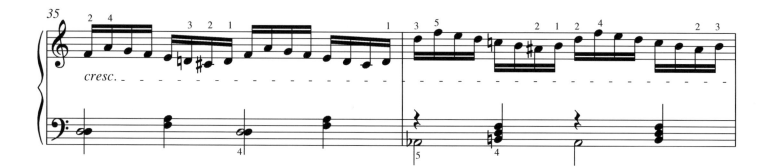

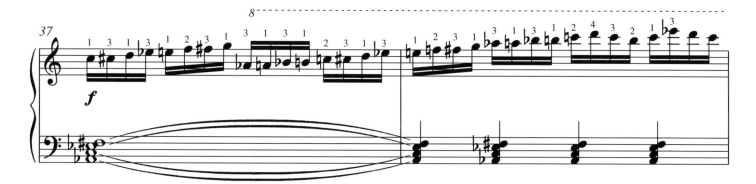

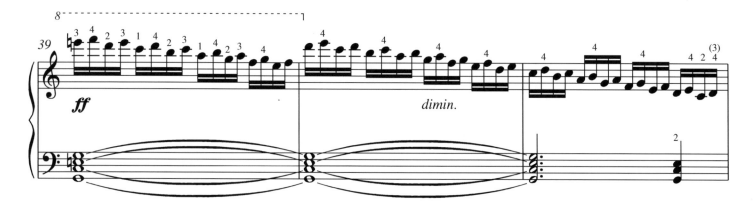

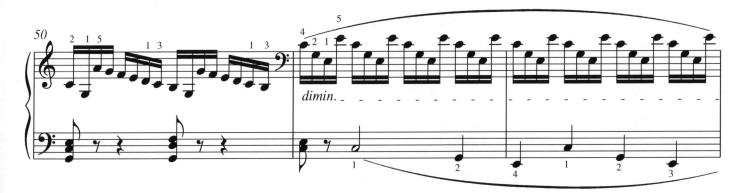

Molto allegro ♩ = 80

9

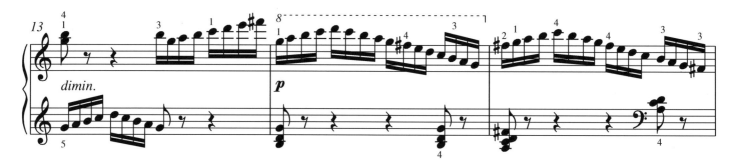

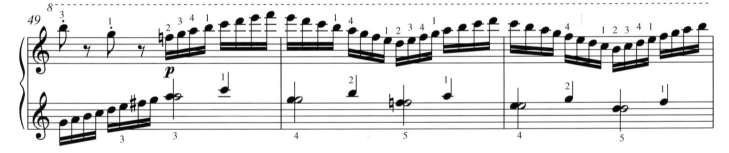

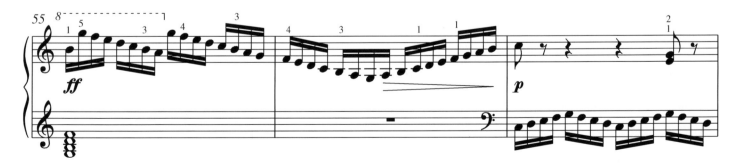

Molto allegro ♩. = 54

10

con anima

legato

Heft 2 / Book 2 / Cahier 2

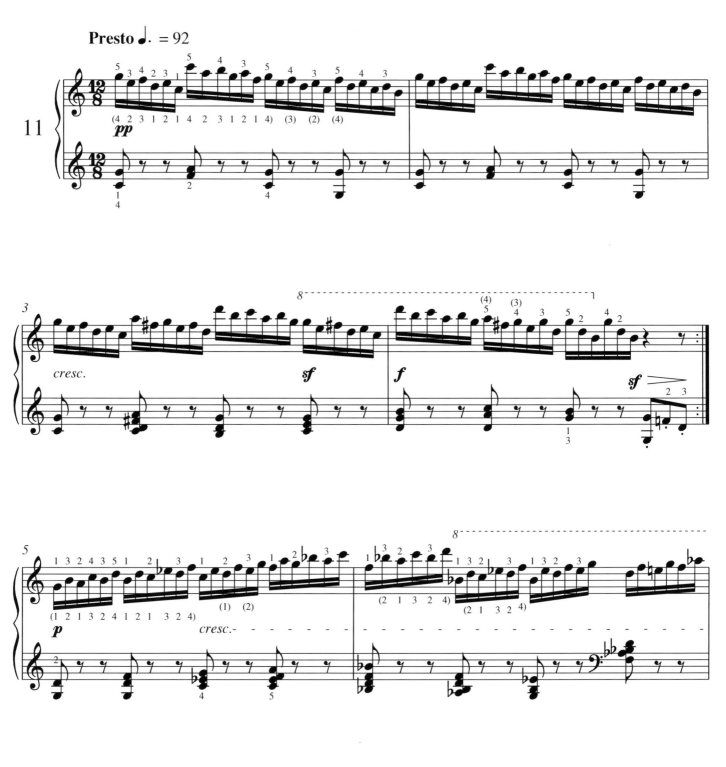

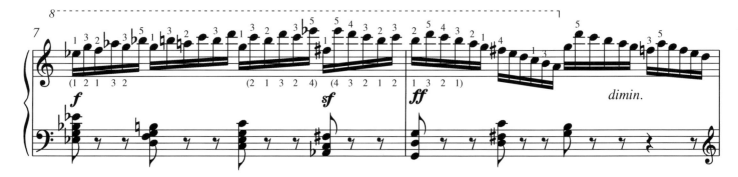

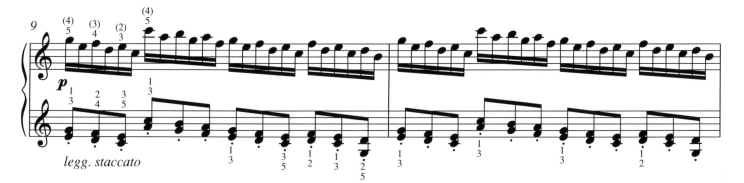

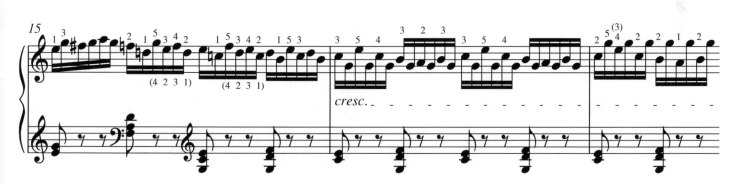

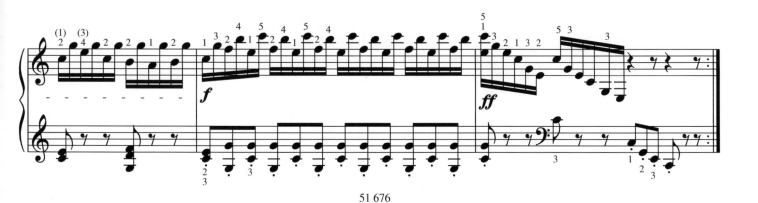

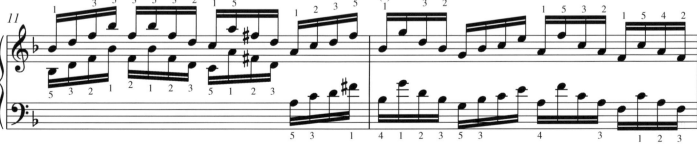

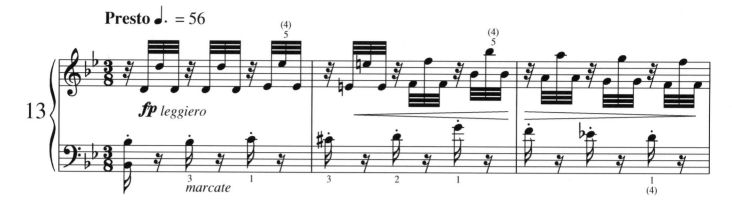

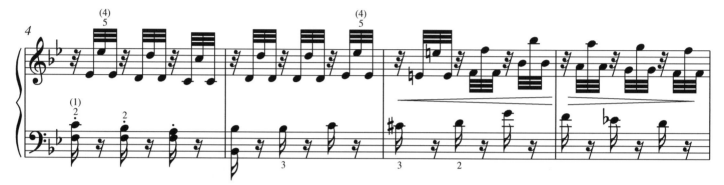

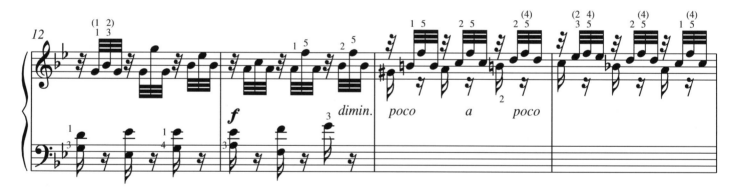

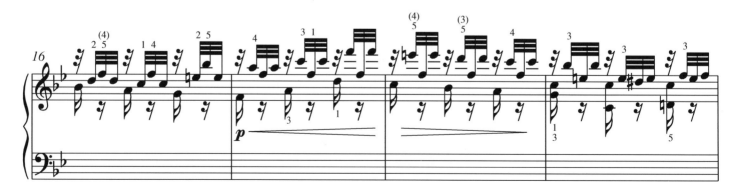

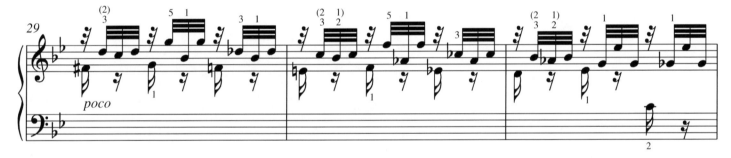

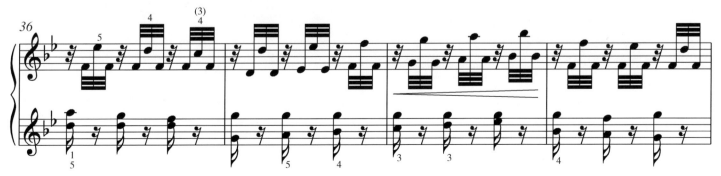

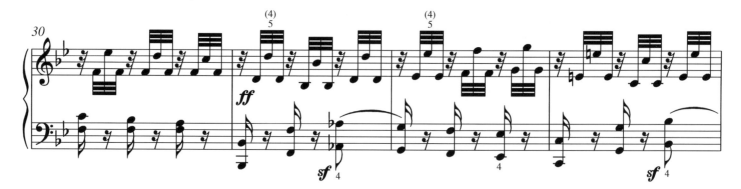

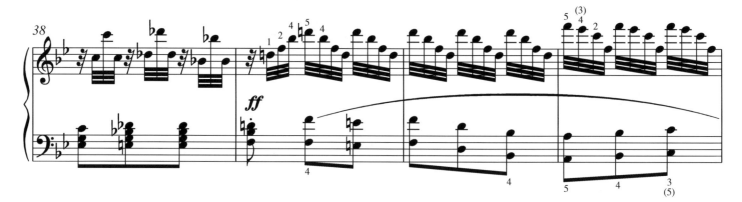

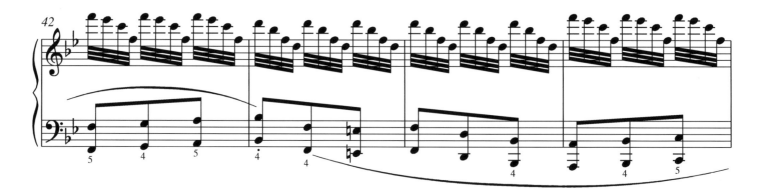

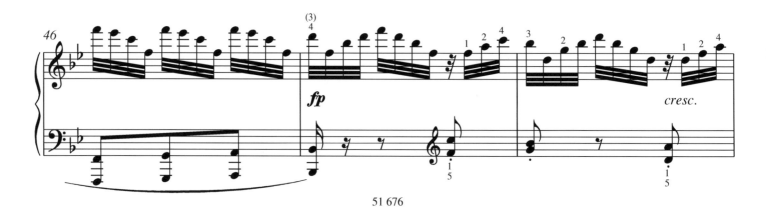

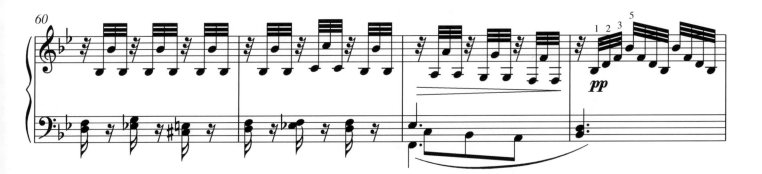

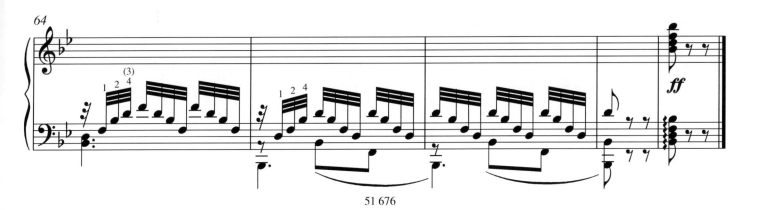

Molto vivo e velocissimo ♪ = 160

14

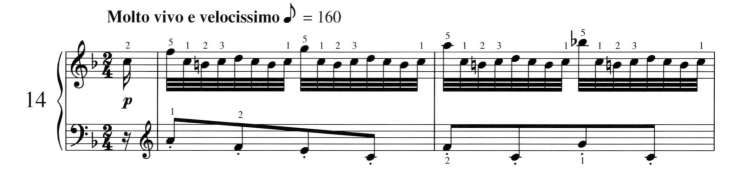

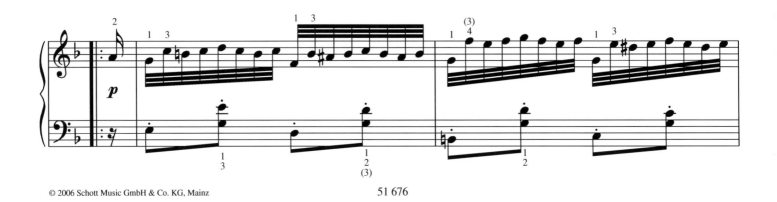

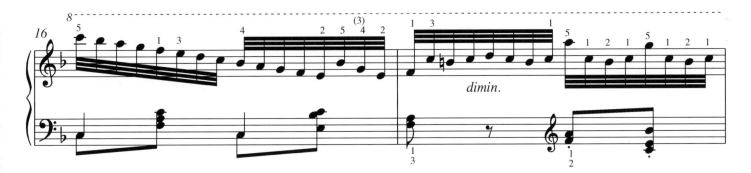

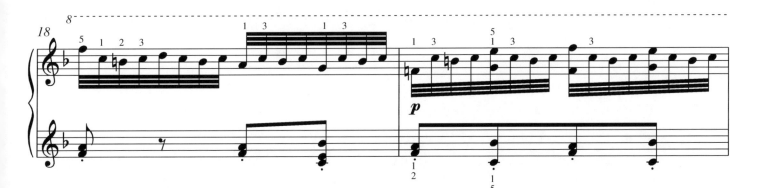

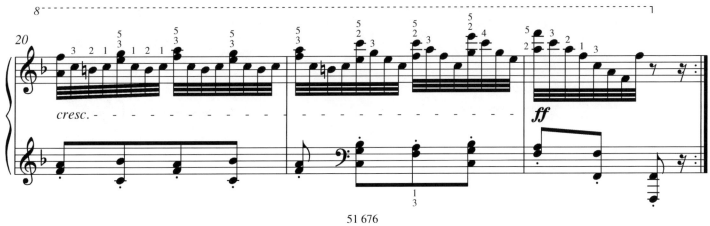

15

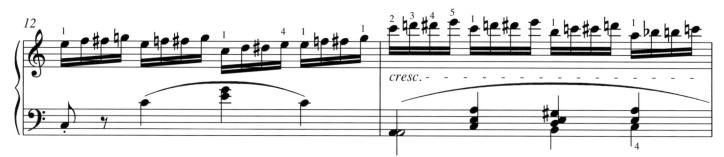

Presto ♩. = 72

16

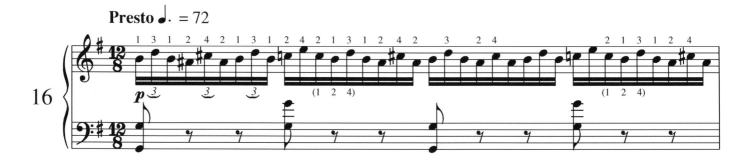

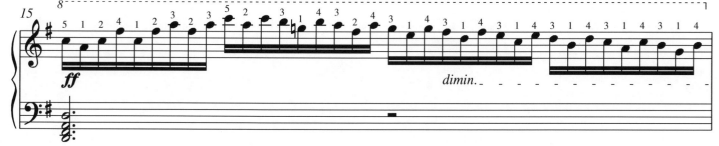

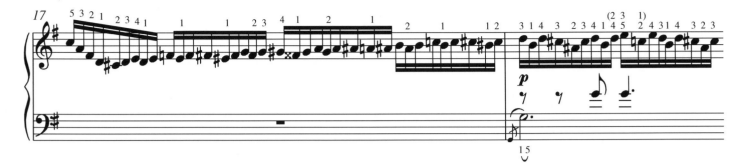

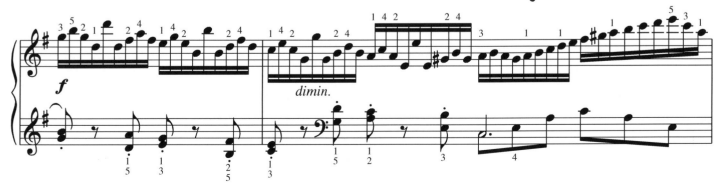

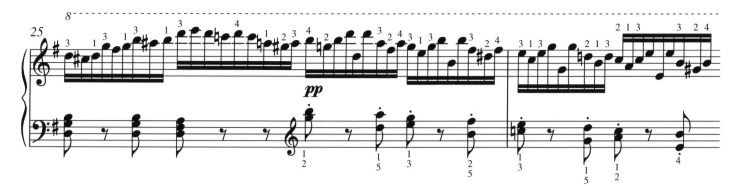

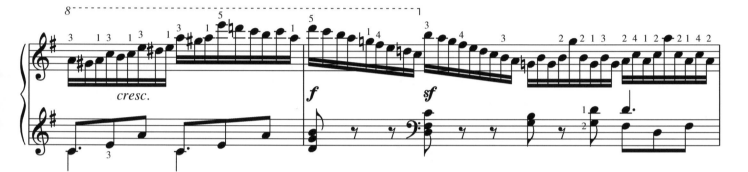

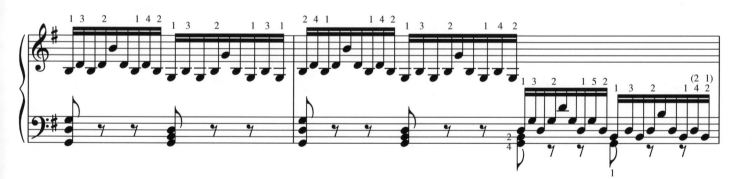

Molto allegro ♩ = 132

17

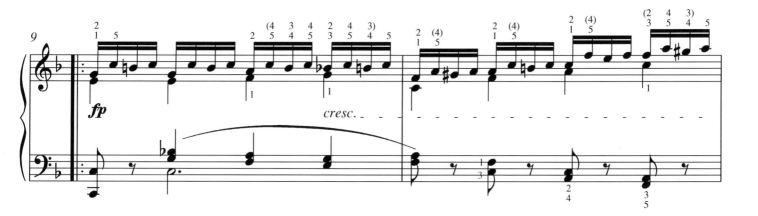

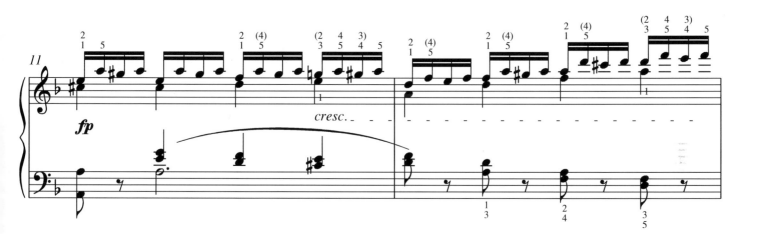

Molto allegro ♩ = 92

18

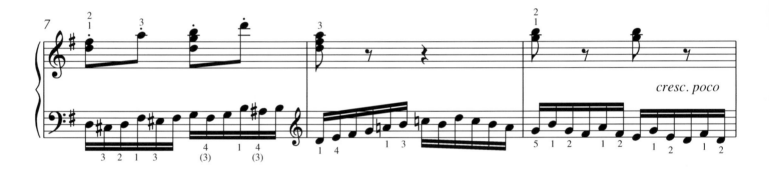

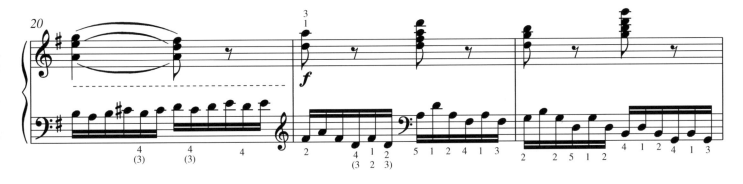

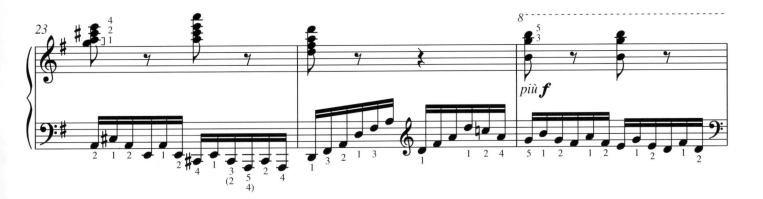

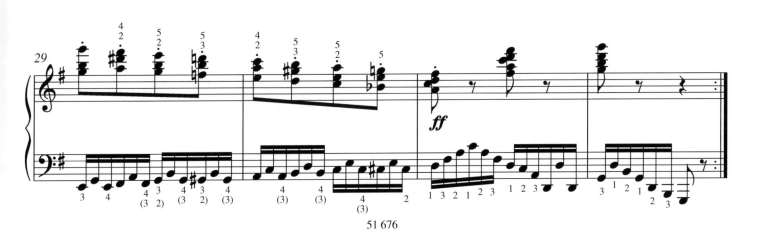

51 676

Presto ♩ = 126

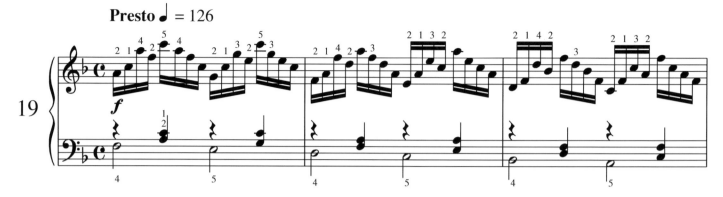

19

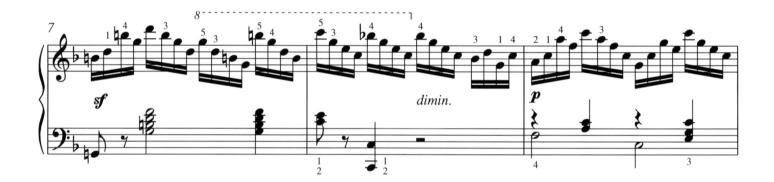

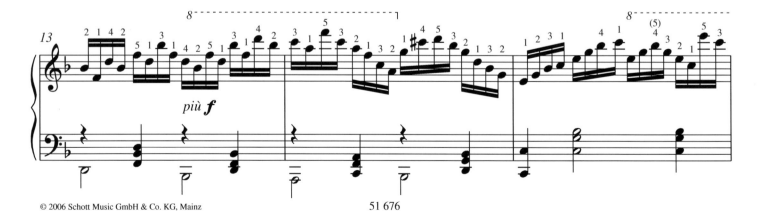

51 676

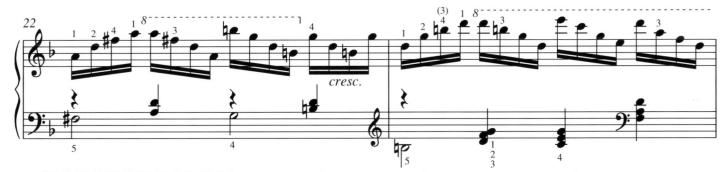

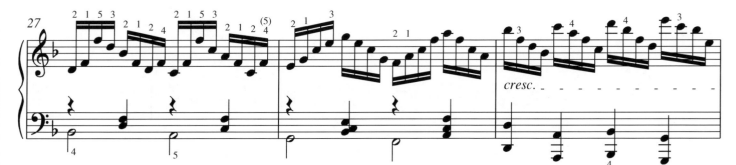

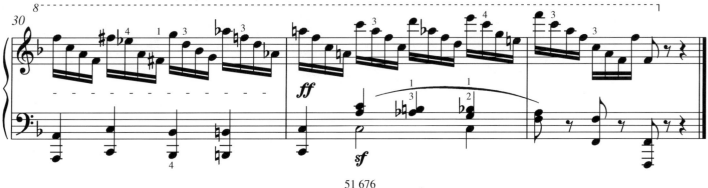

52

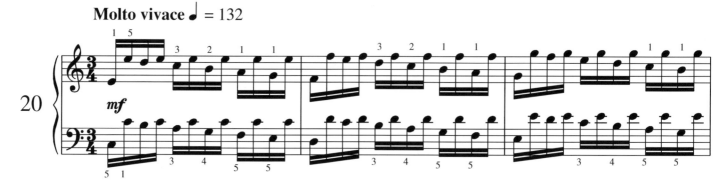

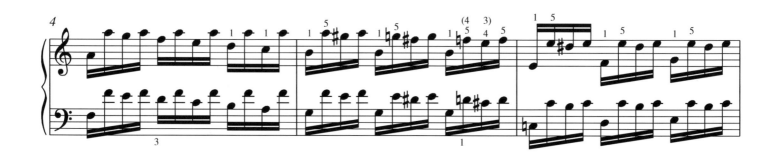

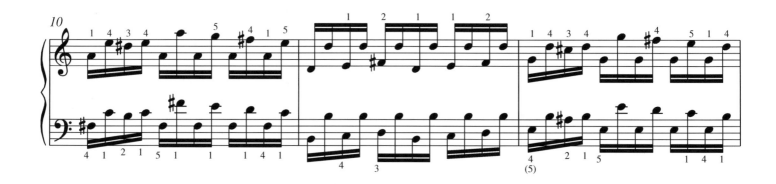

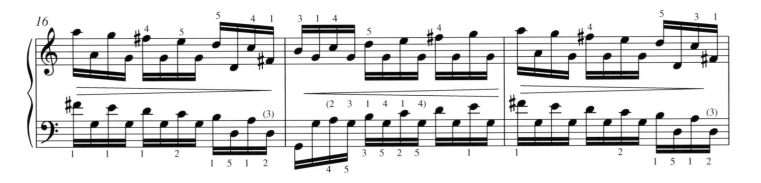

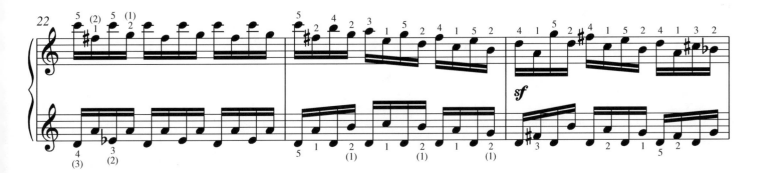

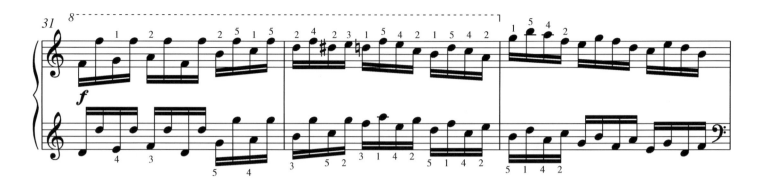

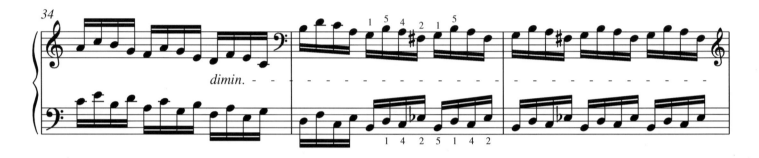

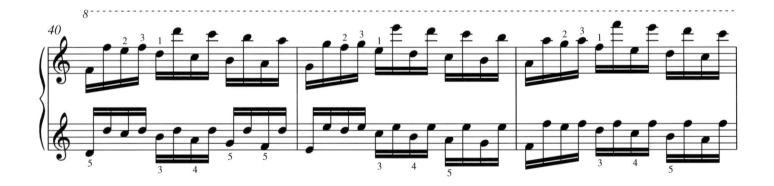

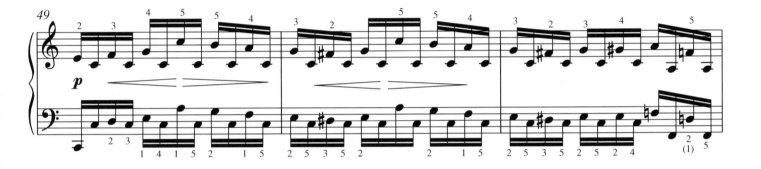

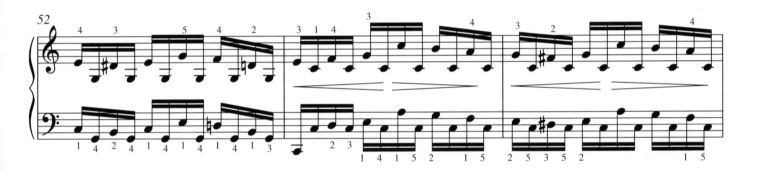

Molto allegro ♩ = 80

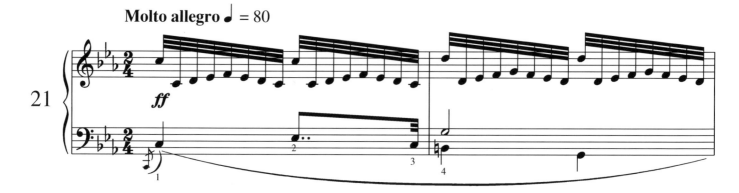

21

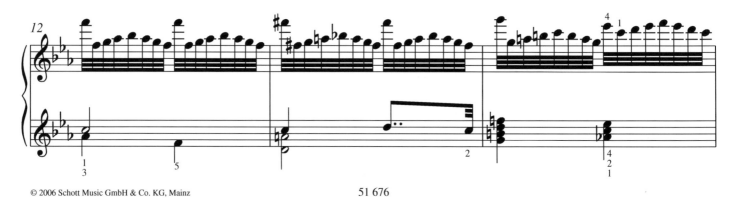

Molto allegro ♩ = 132

22

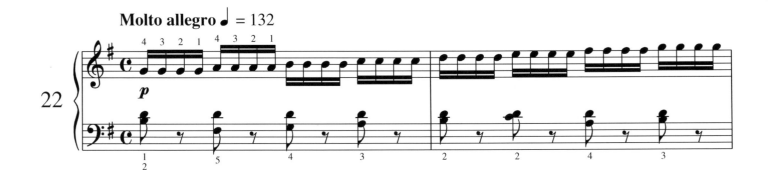

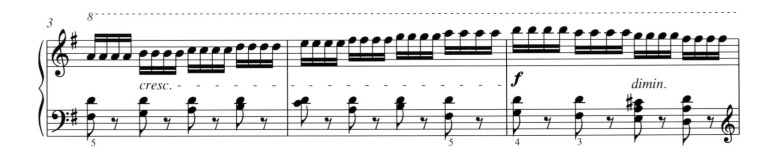

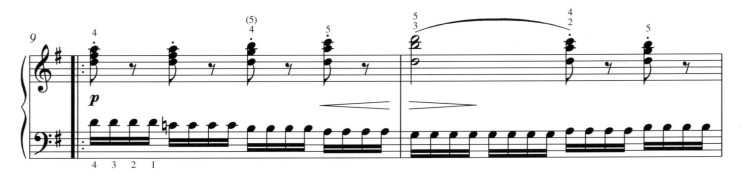

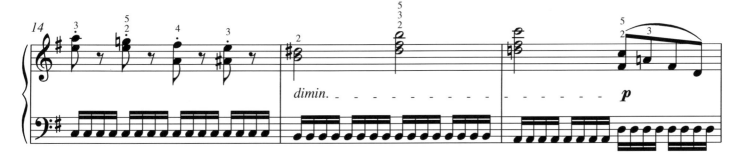

Molto allegro ♩. = 88

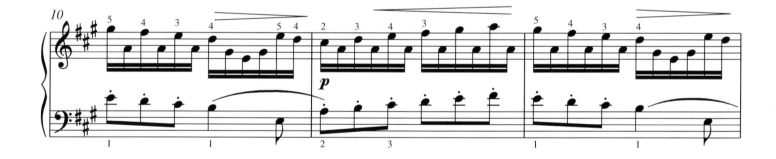

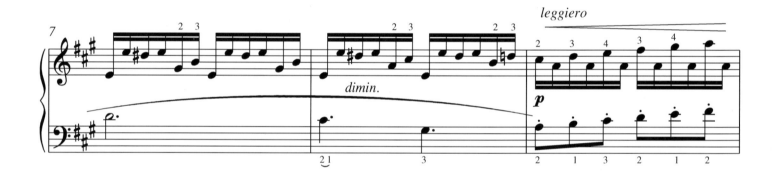

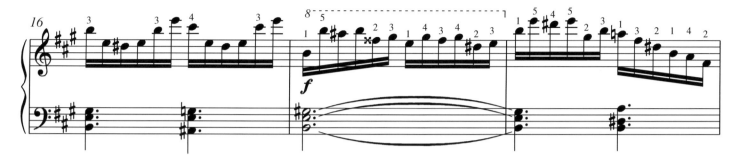

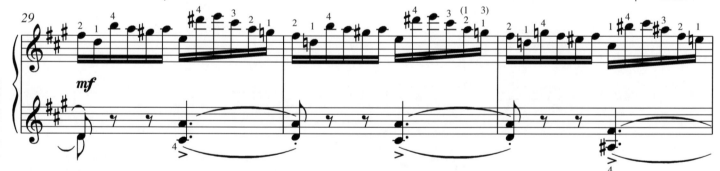

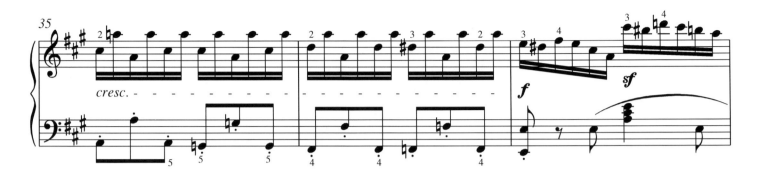

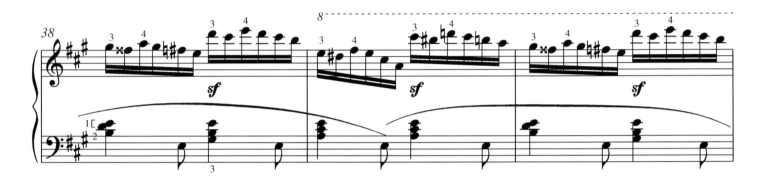

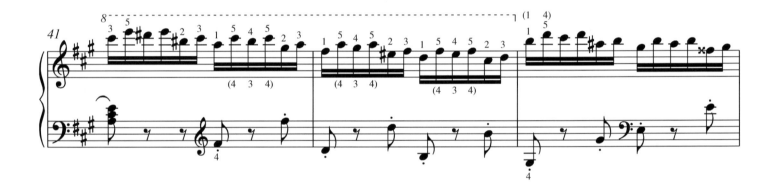

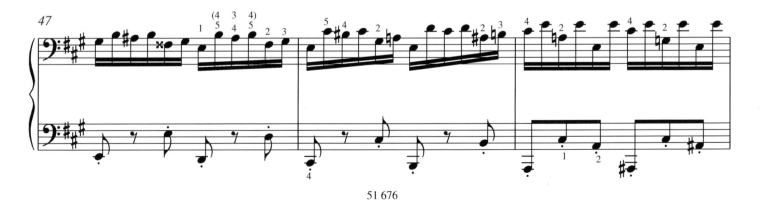

Molto allegro ♩ = 80

24

51 676

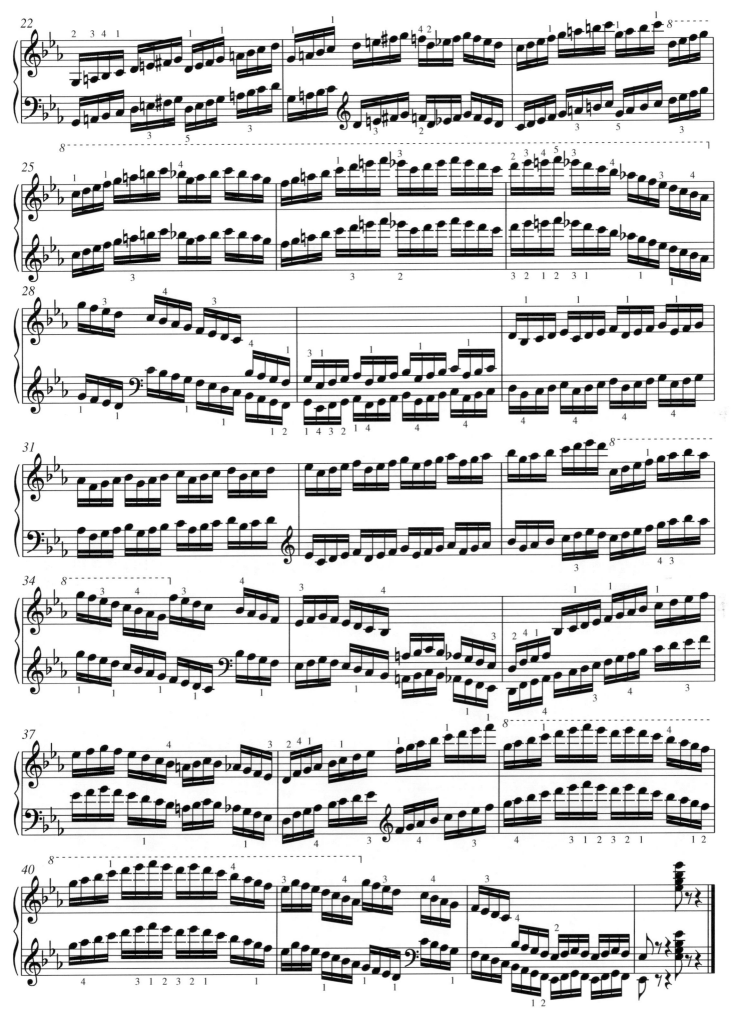

Allegro ♩. = 69

26

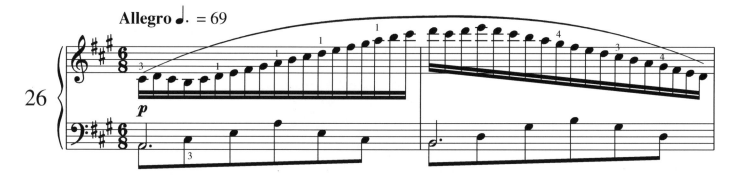

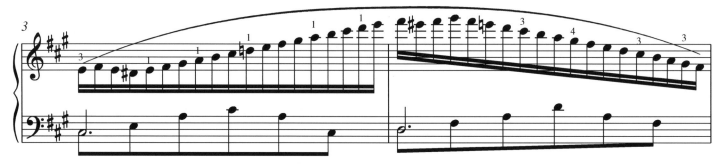

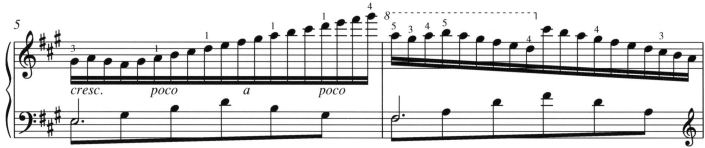

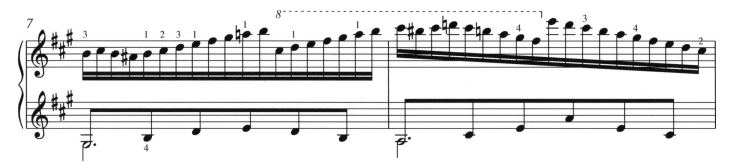

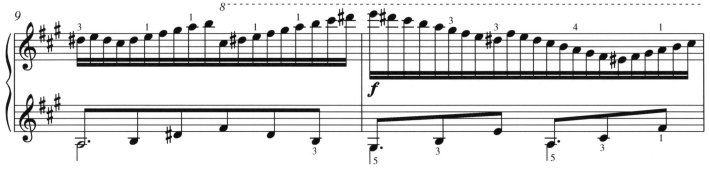

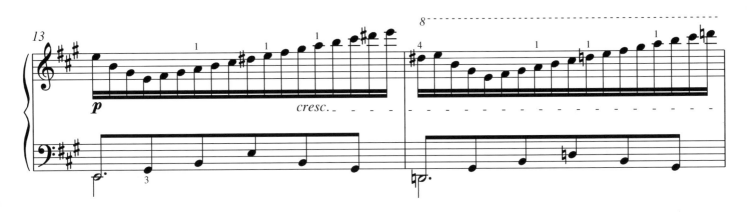

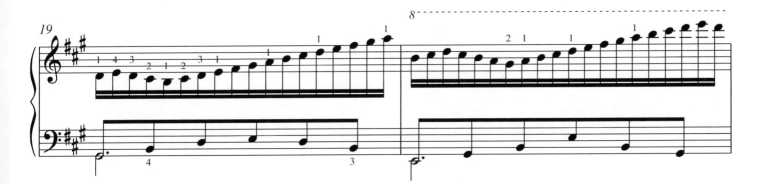

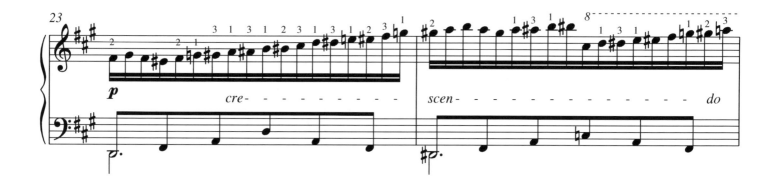

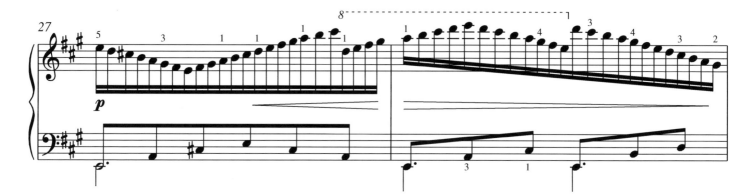

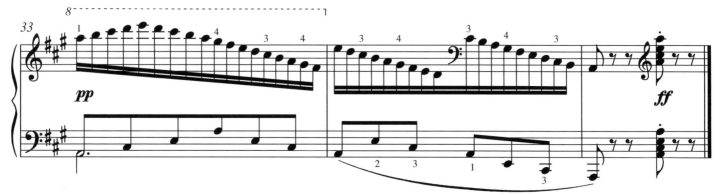

26a

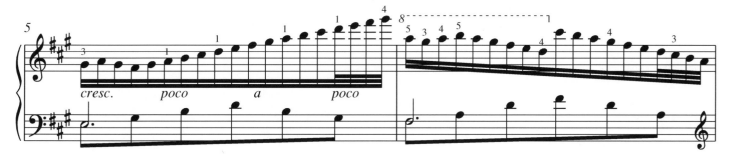

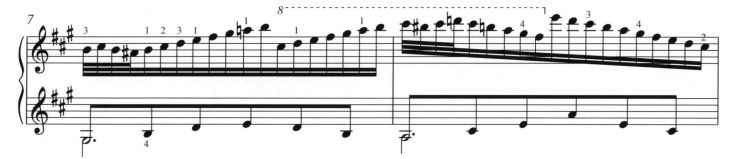

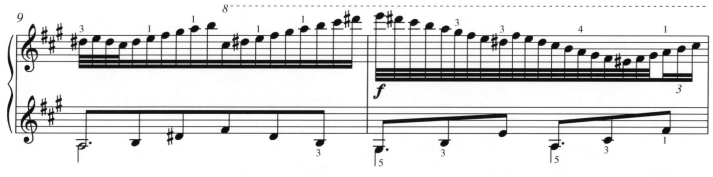

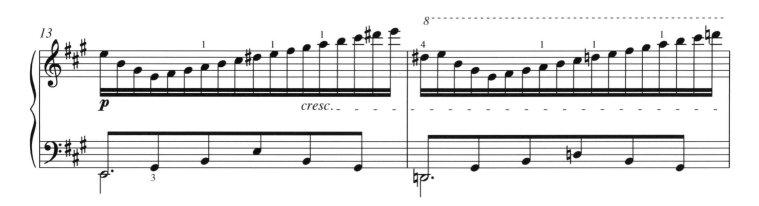

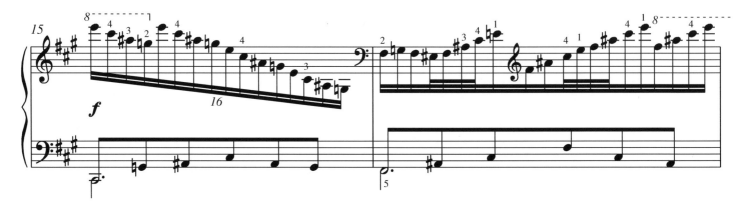

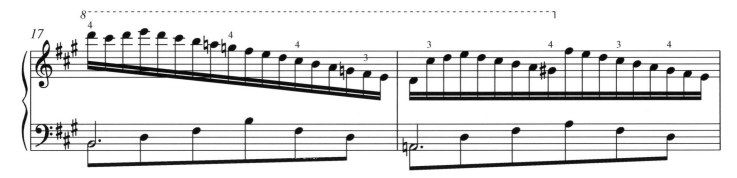

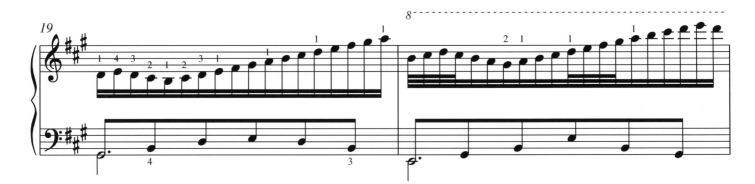

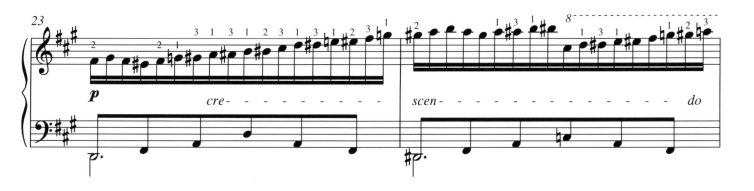

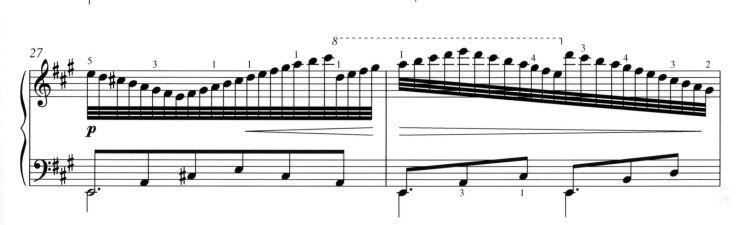

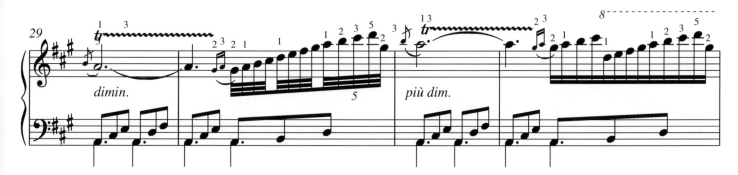

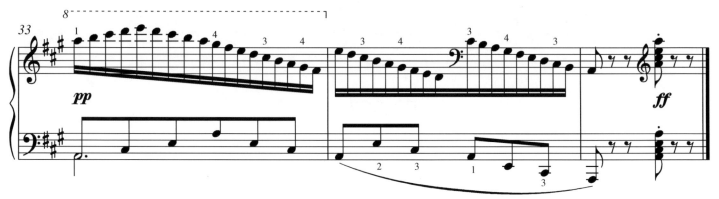

74

Presto ♩ = 152

27

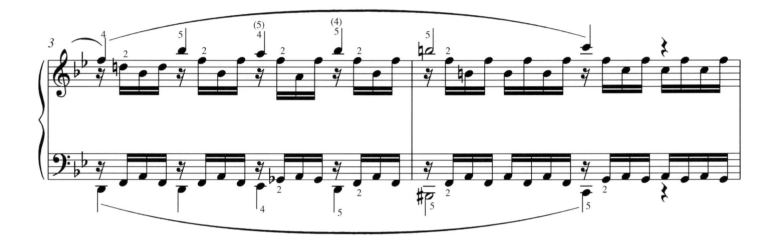

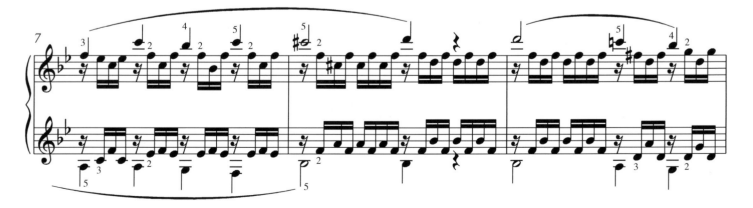

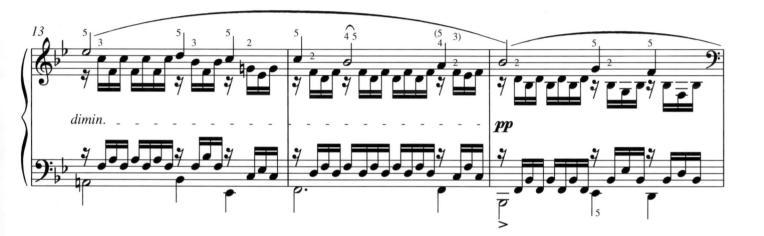

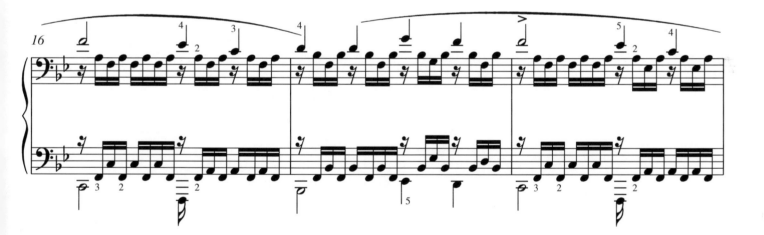

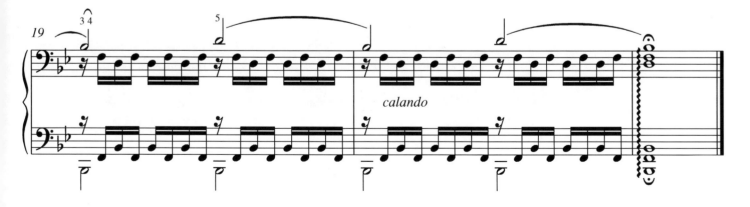

Presto ♩ = 104-112

28

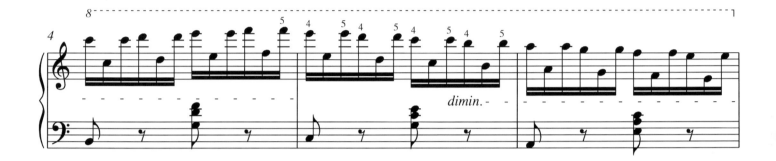

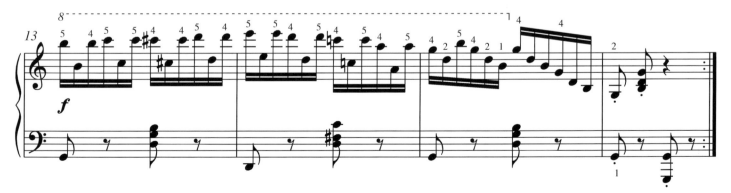

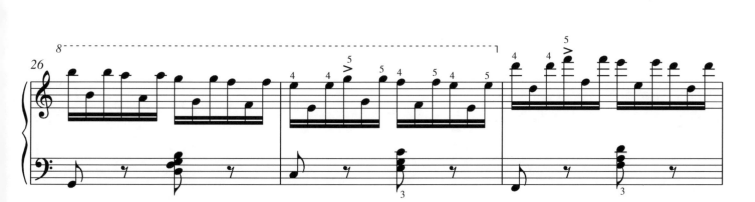

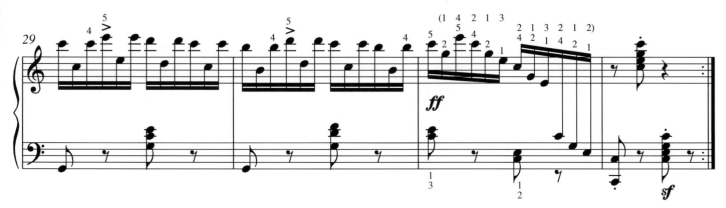

Molto allegro ♩ = 144

29

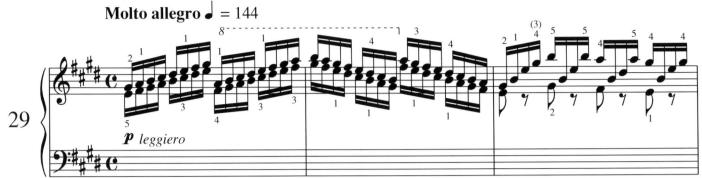

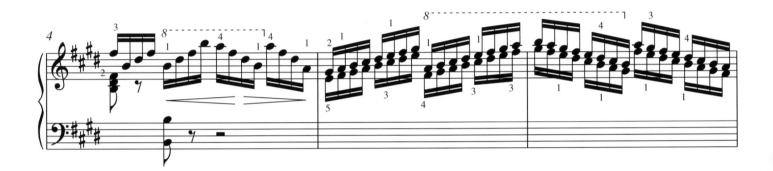

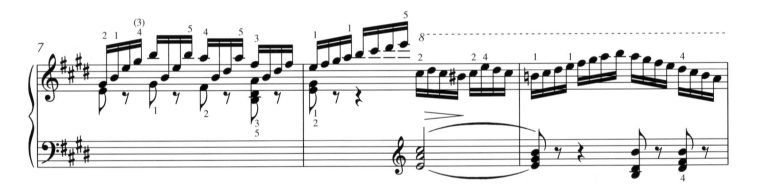

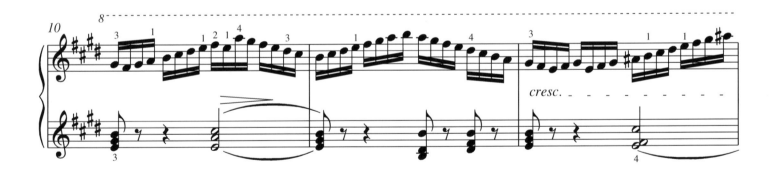

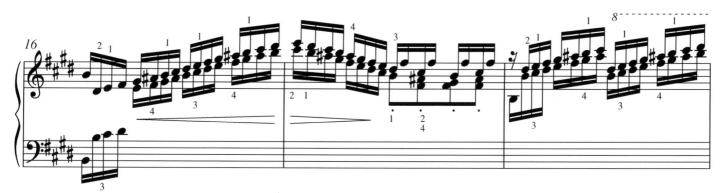

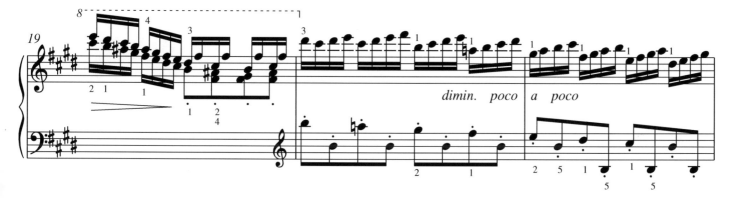

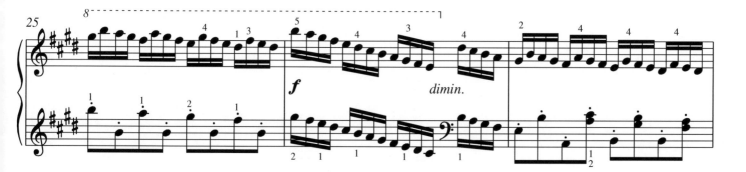

Presto volante ♩. = 58

30

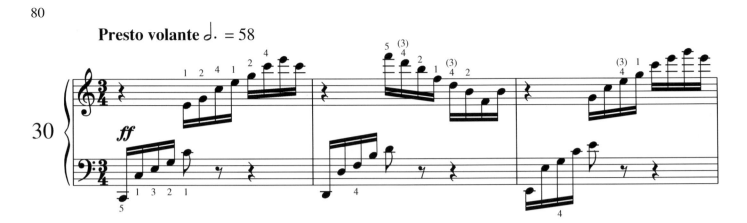

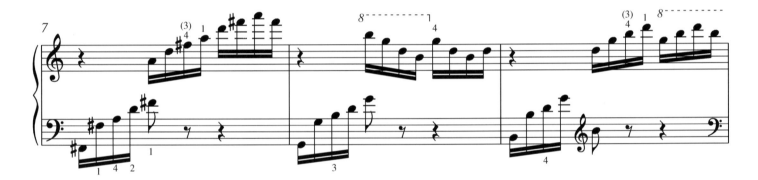

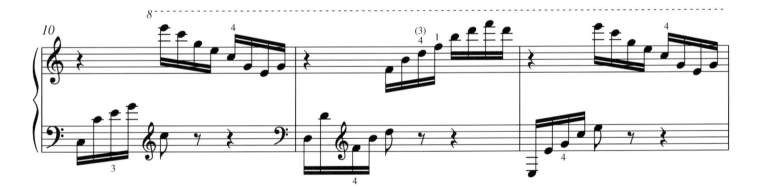

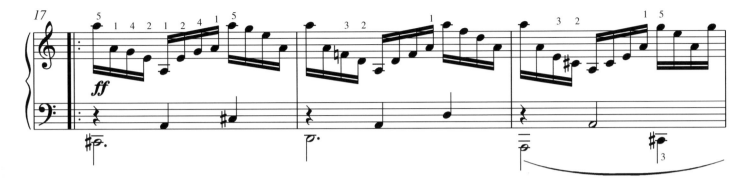

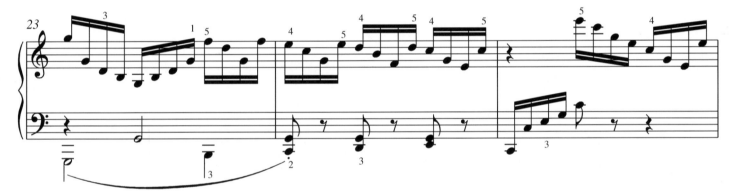

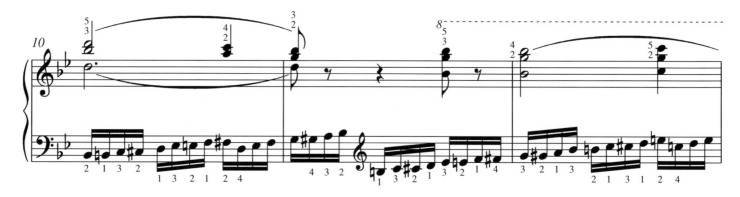

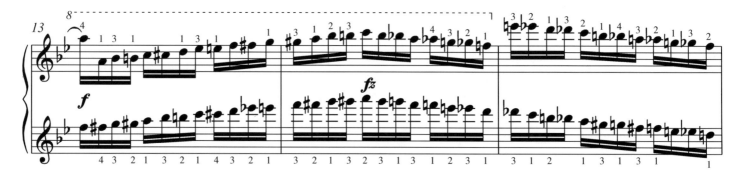

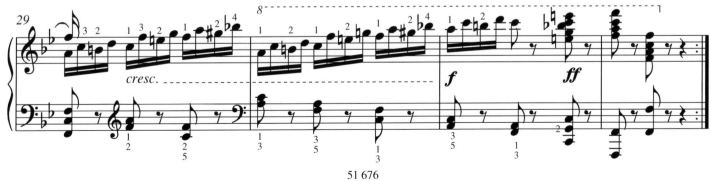

Presto volante ♩ = 88

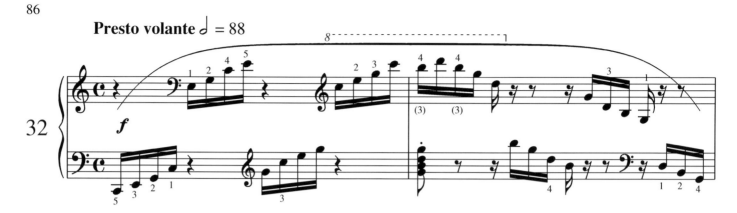

32

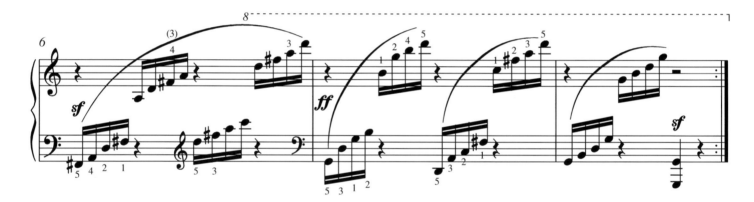

Molto allegro e veloce ♩ = 108

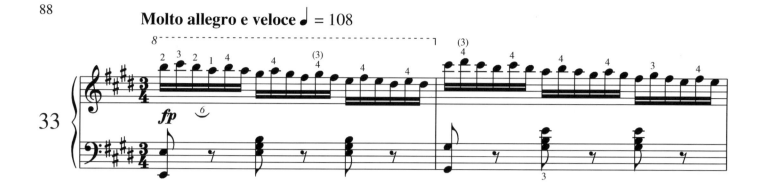

33

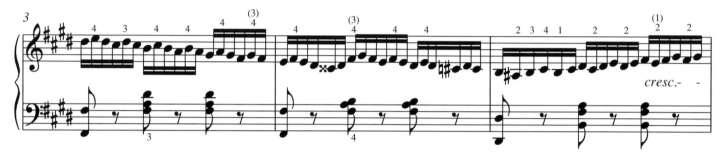

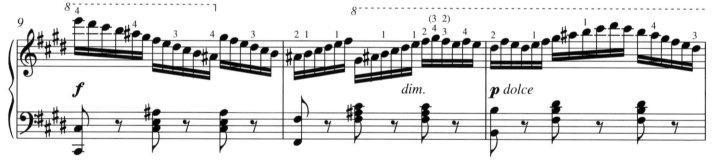

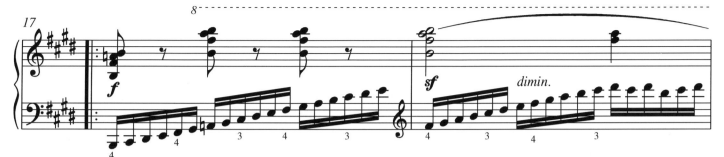

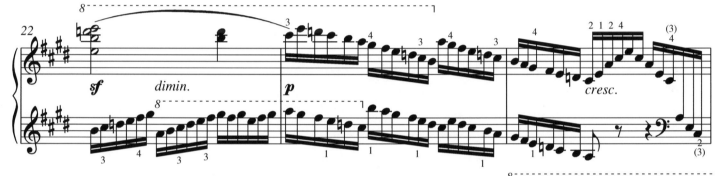

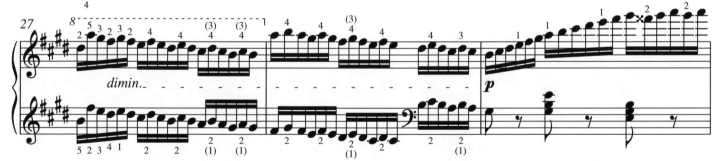

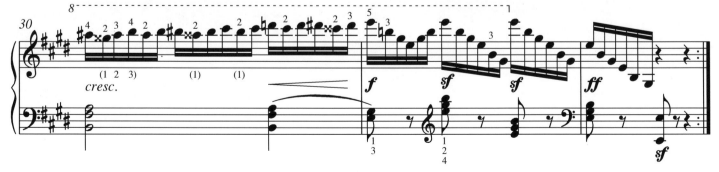

Allegro molto vivo ed energico ♩ = 80

34

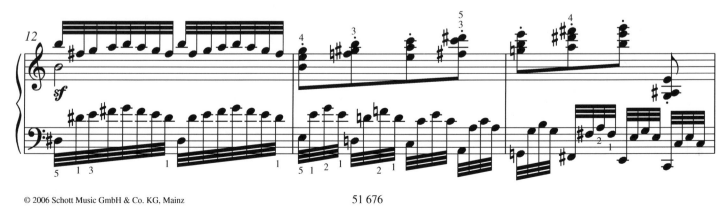

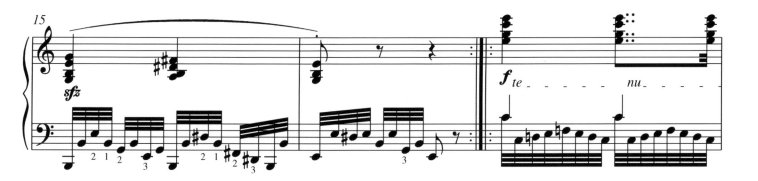

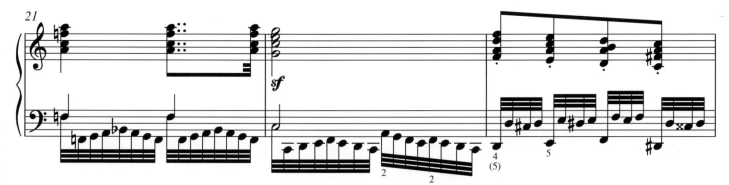

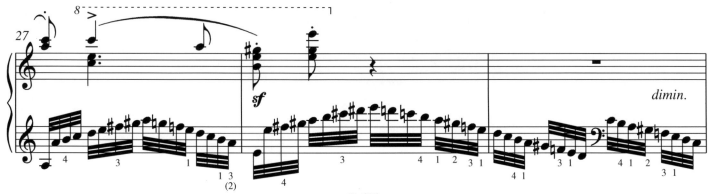

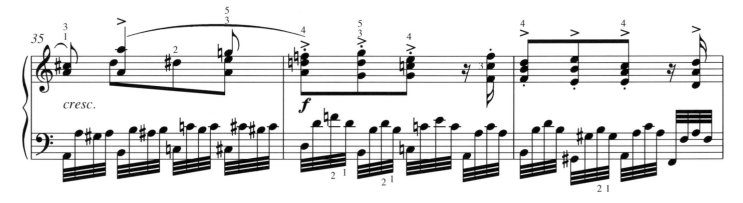

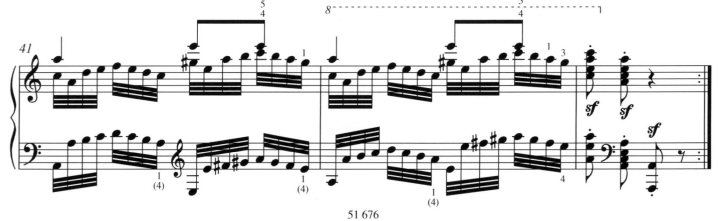

Allegro vivacissimo ♩. = 92

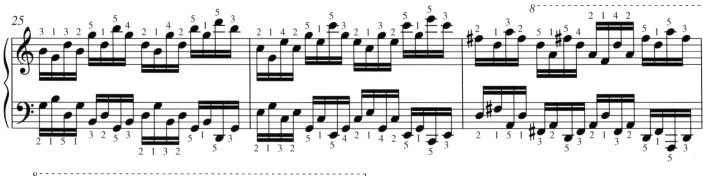

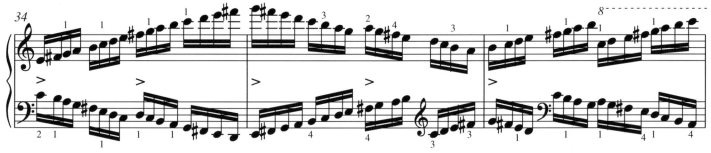

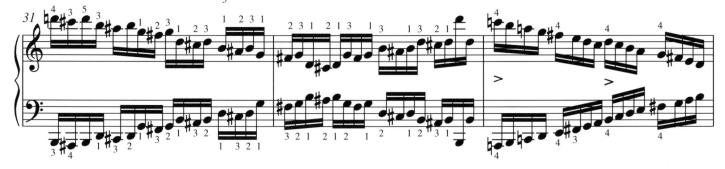

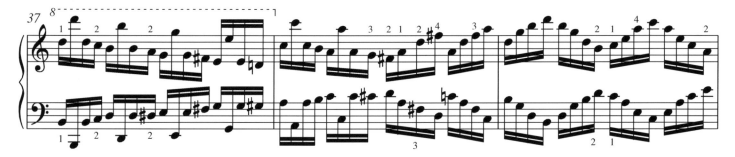

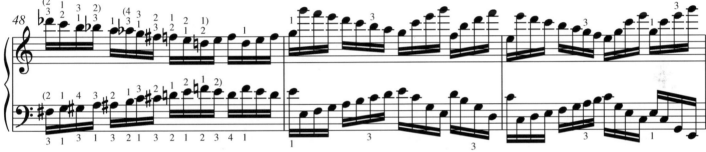

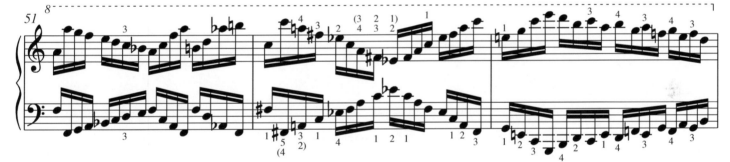

Molto allegro e giocoso ♪ = 138

37

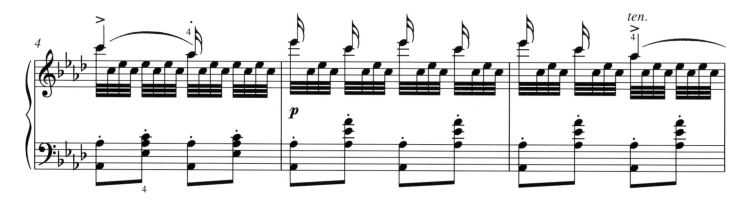

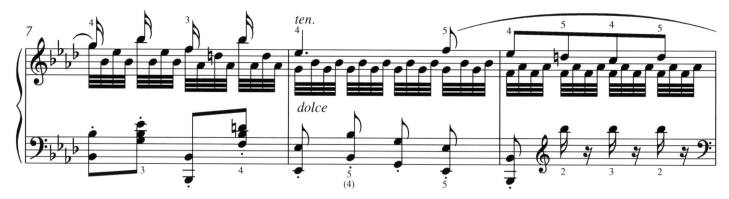

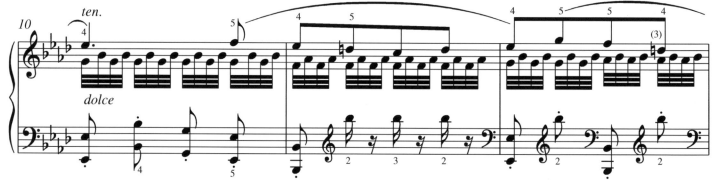

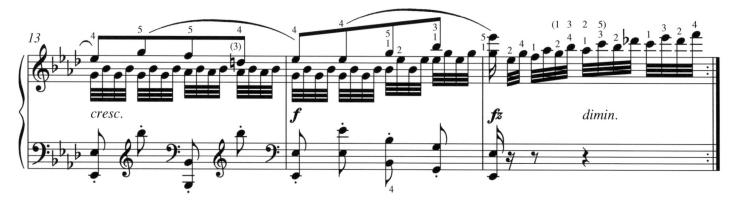

Molto allegro, quasi presto ♩ = 144

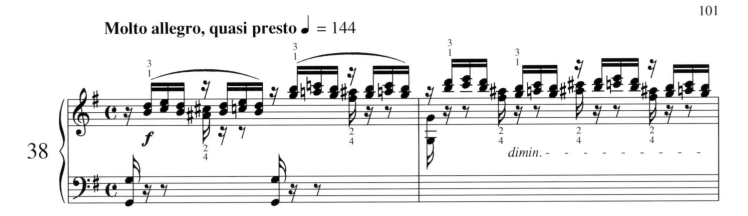

38

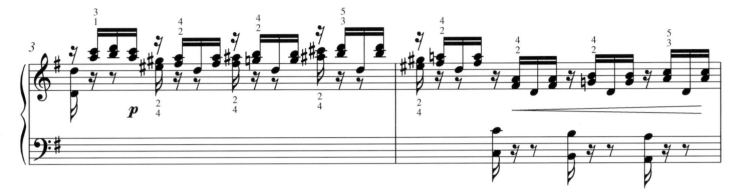

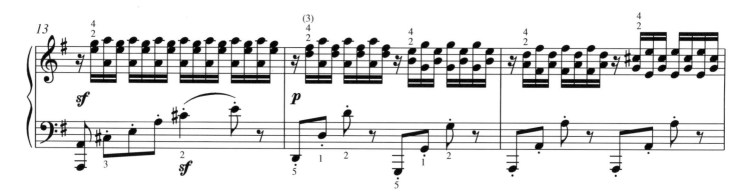

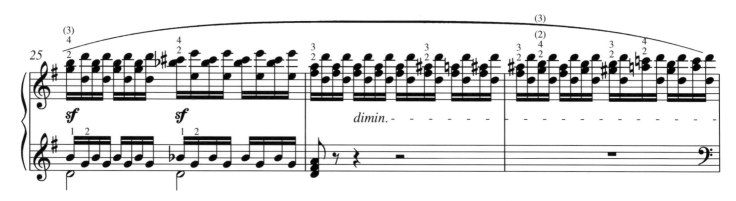

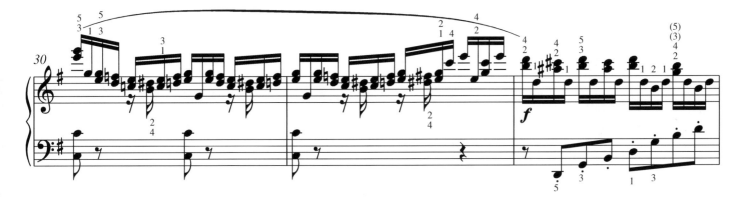

Presto (à la Galopade) ♩ = 80

39

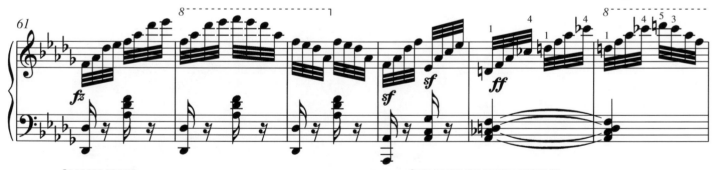

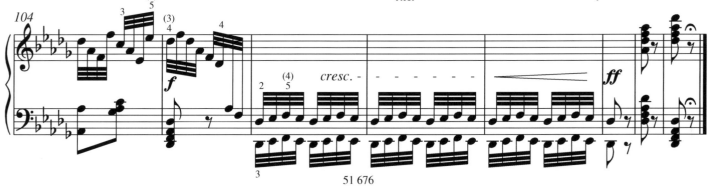

Allegrissimo, quasi presto ♩ = 96

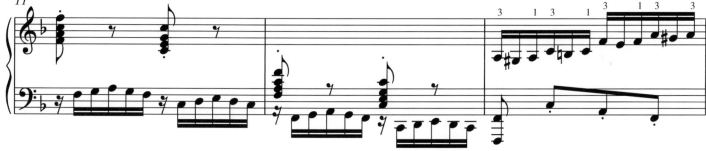

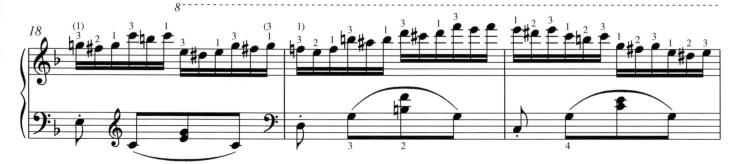

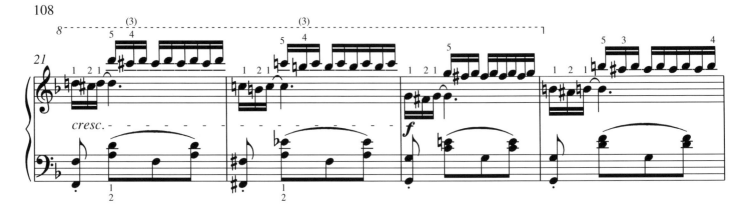

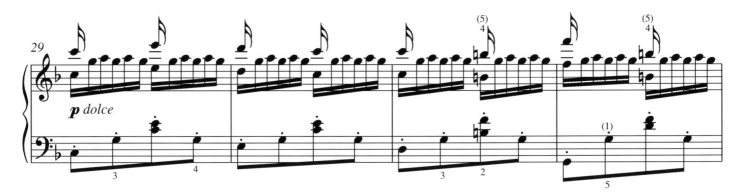

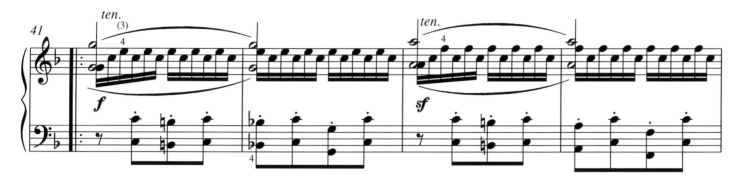

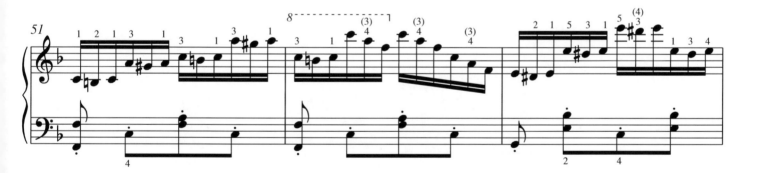

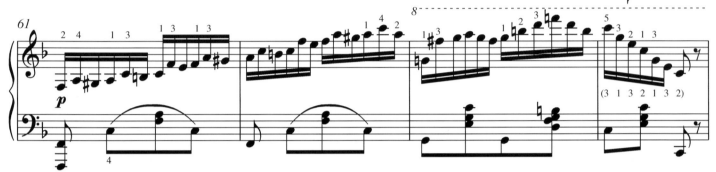

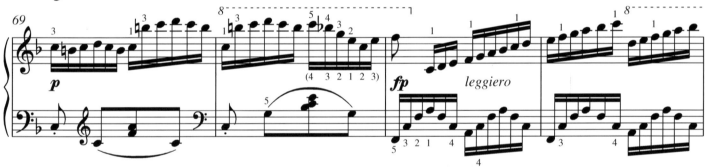

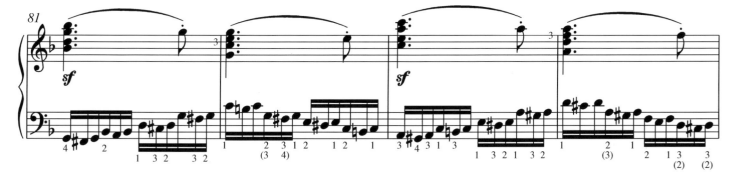

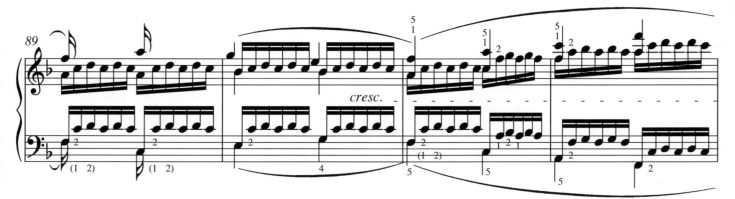

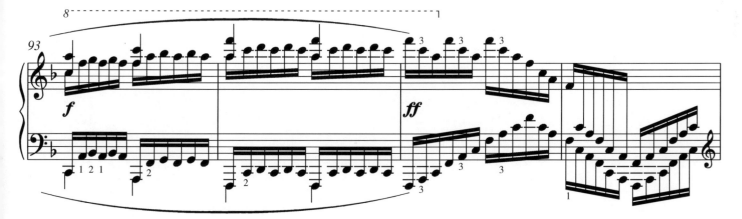

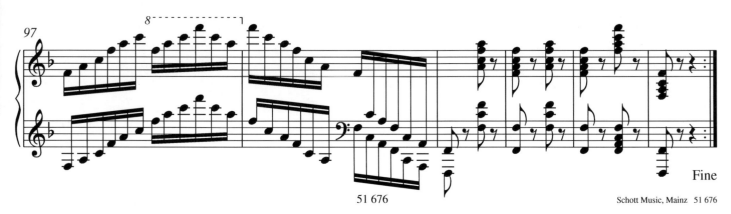

Fine

Schott Music, Mainz 51 676